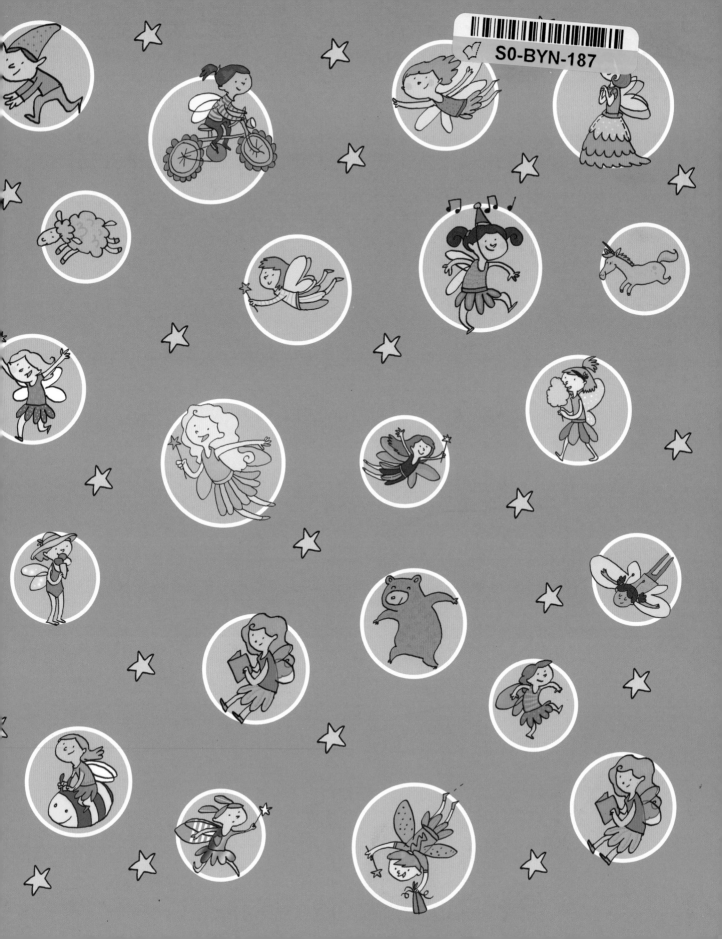

WHO'S HIDING... ∾in∾ Fairyland?

HOTHOUSE

Who's hiding in Fairyland?

Annabelle and Tulip live in Fairyland with all of their magical friends. There's lots of things happening all over the land, from birthday parties to cloud mazes in the sky. Each picture in this book has all sorts of wonderful and interesting things for you to find. In fact, there are over 1000 things to be found in Fairyland! Annabelle and Tulip are in each picture, so you'll need to find them first. Then, each page has little pictures to show you what else you need to look for, from bumblebee space hoppers to rainbow crystals and everything in between! To get you started, can you spot Annabelle and Tulip playing in their magical garden?

Annabelle   Tulip

Can you find all of these items on the opposite page, too?

1 bird's nest   5 ladybugs   10 purple flowers

Toadstool Town

It's a very busy day in Toadstool Town. Annabelle and Tulip have decided to go shopping, can you spot them in the picture below?

Now you've found Tulip and Annabelle, see if you can spot these things, too.

1 toadstool house

2 goblins

3 petal bikes

4 red doors

5 purple birds

6 poppies

7 pogo sticks

8 space hoppers

9 green presents

10 bags of chestnuts

20 blue snails

Flower Festival

There's a flower festival in Fairyland today. Can you find Fairies Tulip and Annabelle amongst all of their friends?

Now you've found Tulip and Annabelle, see if you can spot these things, too.

1 pink unicorn

2 squirrels

3 flutes

4 dancing mice

5 toffee apples

6 frogs

7 smiley red flowers

8 candy floss

9 yellow stars

10 purple sweeties

20 red hearts

Fairy Queen's Party

It's the Fairy Queen's birthday and everyone in Fairyland is having a party. Can you find fairies Annabelle and Tulip?

4 red balloons

5 chocolate puddings

6 lanterns

7 pink present

Can you find all of these other items at the party, too?

1 birthday cake

2 petal thrones

3 blue butterflies

8 sandwiches

9 red roses

10 party hats

20 flower cookies

Crystal Cascades

It's a very hot day and all of the fairies are cooling down at the Crystal Cascades. Can you spot Fairy Annabelle and Fairy Tulip?

Now you've found Tulip and Annabelle, see if you can spot these things, too.

1 sweetie shop

2 flamingos

3 lotion bottles

4 rubber rings

5 red swimsuits

6 pairs of green sunglasses

7 ice creams

8 floppy hats

9 yellow lizzards

10 starfish

20 pink pebbles

Rainbow Meadow

There's a rainbow stretching all across the meadow today. Can you spot Annabelle and Tulip amongst their fairy friends?

4 naughty pixies

5 brown bears

6 skipping ropes

7 pink sheep

Can you find all of these other items in the meadow, too?

1 volley ball

2 candy canes

3 bags of crystals

8 pots of gold

9 purple tulips

10 paw prints

20 bumble bees

Fairy Forest

The fairies are having lots of fun flying in and out of the trees in Firefly Forest. Can you spot Fairy Annabelle and Fairy Tulip amongst their friends?

Now you've found Tulip and Annabelle, see if you can spot these things, too.

1 camp fire

2 foxes

3 racoons

4 bunnies

5 wood sprites

6 pixies

7 musical notes

8 purple moths

9 blue daisies

10 beetles

20 glow worms

Enchanted Lagoon

Tulip and Annabelle have come to the lagoon to cool and off and play with all of their friends. Can you find them?

4 purple bats

5 pink shells

6 lilypads

7 frogs

Can you find all of these other items at the lagoon, too?

1 love heart boat

2 mermaids

3 turtles

8 rainbow fish

9 pond skater bugs

10 bubbles

20 fireflies

Treetop School

There is plenty going on at school today.
Can you spot fairies Annabelle and Tulip?

Can you find these other things up in the treetop, too?

1 griffin

2 flower clocks

3 owls

4 leaf swings

5 purple bags

6 pencil cases

7 calculators with wings

8 prefect badges

9 green books

10 pink leaves

20 ants

Fairy Show

Some of the fairies are putting on a show.
Can you find Annabelle and Tulip amongst
all of their fairy friends?

Fairy
Show

4 pink microphones

5 blue spot lights

6 torches

7 cobwebs

Can you find all of these other items in the show, too?

1 tuba

2 purple curtains

3 violins

3 tubs of popcorn

9 bottles of water

10 purple slugs

20 roses

Cloud Maze

The fairies are playing up in the clouds. Can you spot fairies Annabelle and Tulip amongst their friends?

START

FINISH

Now you've found Tulip and Annabelle, see if you can spot these things, too.

1 flying trophy

2 flying horses

3 red hats

4 mice riding birds

5 scooters

6 green kites

7 pink clouds

8 blue flags

9 windmills

10 pairs of shorts

20 raindrops

Well done, you've found everything in Fairyland! Now go back and see if you can find each of these extra items in every picture, too.

1 Fairy Queen

1 mushroom

1 yellow sweetie

1 centaur

1 green tulip

1 flag with a clover

1 daisy parasol

1 venus fly trap

1 swirly lollypop

1 fairy with spotty wings

1 humming bird

How closely were you looking? Do you know which picture each of these items were in?

10 cupcakes

10 blue diamonds

10 acorn lunchboxes

10 shooting stars

10 rainbow butterflies

10 radios

10 pairs of binoculars

10 millipedes

10 rose perfume

10 toy bunnies